christmas crackers

Production: Stephen Clark and Sadie Cook

Published 1994

© **International Music Publications Limited**
Southend Road, Woodford Green, Essex IG8 8HN, England

ALL I WANT FOR CHRISTMAS IS
MY TWO FRONT TEETH

Words and Music by
DON GARDNER

ANOTHER ROCK & ROLL CHRISTMAS

Words and Music by
LEANDER, SEAGO and GLITTER

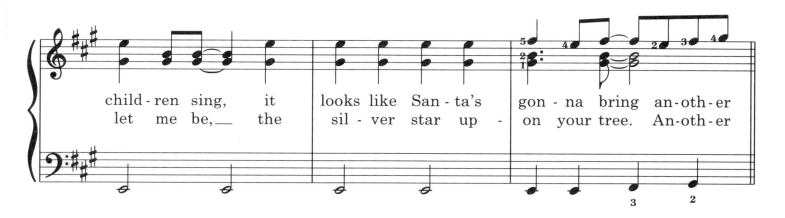

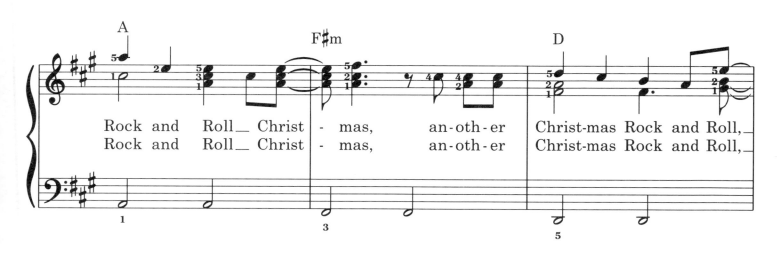

rock-ing   in your   stock-ing   when you   see your big sur - prise,   'cos I'll be

rock-ing   in your   stock-ing,   you   won't be-lieve your   big blue eyes.

CHRISTMAS ALPHABET

Words and Music by
BUDDY KAYE and JULES LOMAN

THE CHRISTMAS SONG
(CHESTNUTS ROASTING ON AN OPEN FIRE)

Words and Music by
MEL TORME and ROBERT WELLS

LAST CHRISTMAS

Words and Music by
GEORGE MICHAEL

This year_ to save me from tears_ I'll give it to some-one spe-

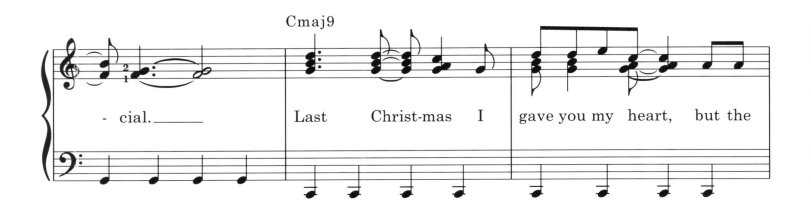

-cial._____ Last Christ-mas I gave you my heart, but the

ve-ry next day you gave it a-way.__ This year_ to

save me from tears_ I'll give it to some-one spe - cial._____

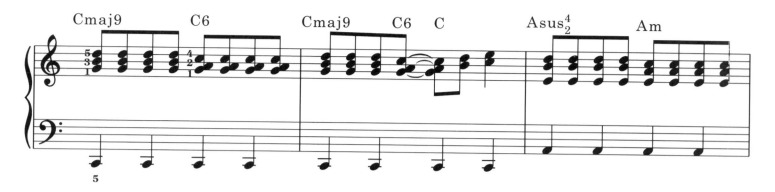

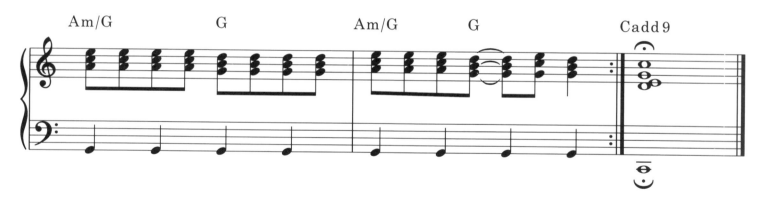

Once bitten and twice shy
I keep my distance but you still catch my eye.
Tell me baby, do you recognise me?
Well, it's been a year, it doesn't surprise me.
(Happy Christmas!)
I wrapped it up and sent it
With a note saying "I love you," I meant it.
Now I know what a fool I've been
But if you kissed me now I know you'd fool me again.

A crowded room, friends with tired eyes,
I'm hiding from you and your soul of ice.
My God! I thought you were someone to rely on.
Me? I guess I was a shoulder to cry on.
A face on a lover with a fire in his heart,
A man undercover but you tore me apart,
Now I've found a real love you'll never fool me again.

HAVE YOURSELF A
MERRY LITTLE CHRISTMAS

Words and Music by
HUGH MARTIN and RALPH BLANE

I SAW MOMMY KISSING SANTA CLAUS

Words and Music by
TOMMIE CONNOR

JINGLE BELLS

TRADITIONAL

2. Now the ground is white
   Go it while you're young.
   Take the girls tonight,
   Sing this sleighing song.
   Get a bob-tailed bay,
   Two-forty for his speed.
   Then hitch him to an open sleigh
   And you will take the lead.
   Jingle bells, etc.

LET IT SNOW!
LET IT SNOW! LET IT SNOW!

Words by SAMMY CAHN
Music by JULE STYNE

23

LITTLE DONKEY

Words and Music by
ERIC BOSWELL

LITTLE DRUMMER BOY

Words and Music by HARRY SIMEONE,
HENRY ONORATI and KATHERINE K DAVIS

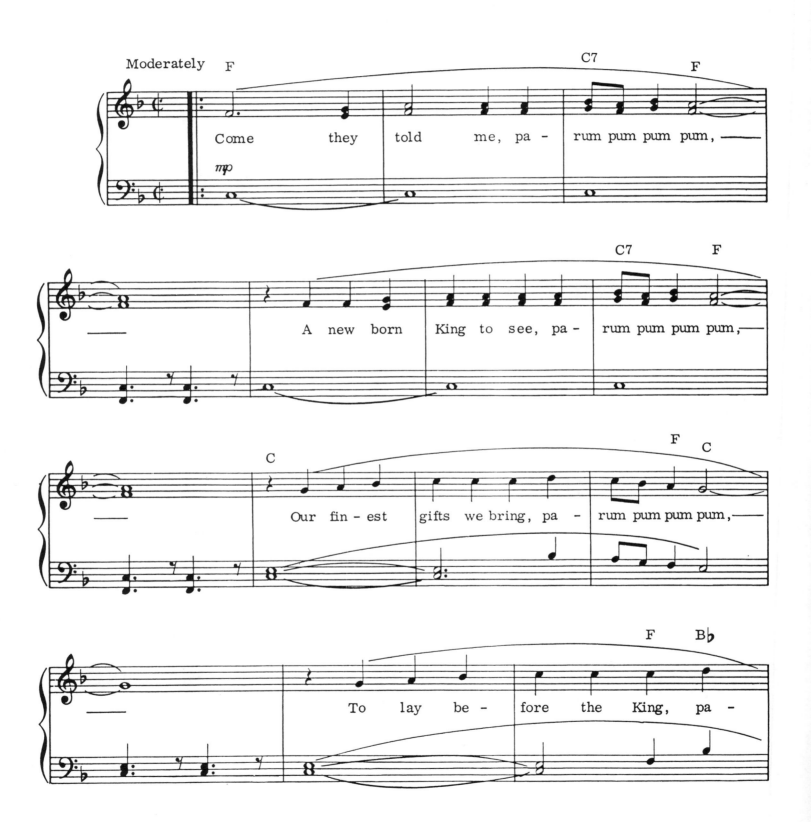

rum pum pum pum,   rum pum pum pum,   rum pum pum pum, ——

So   to   hon - our Him,   pa - rum pum pum   pum, ——

when— we   come. ——

2. Little Baby, pa-rum pum pum pum,
   I am a poor boy too, pa-rum pum pum pum,
   I have no gift to bring, pa-rum pum pum pum,
   That's fit to give our King, pa-rum pum pum pum,
   Rum pum pum pum, rum pum pum pum,
   Shall I play for you, pa-rum pum pum pum,
   On my drum?

3. Mary nodded, pa-rum pum pum pum,
   The Ox and Lamb kept time, pa-rum pum pum pum,
   I played my drum for Him, pa-rum pum pum pum,
   I played my best for Him, pa-rum pum pum pum,
   Rum pum pum pum, rum pum pum pum,
   Then He smiled at me, pa-rum pum pum pum,
   Me and my drum.

MARY'S BOY CHILD

Words and Music by
JESTER HAIRSTON

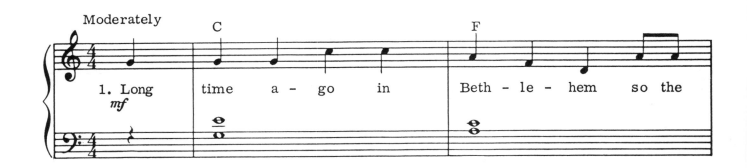

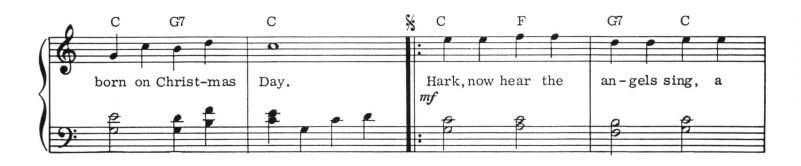

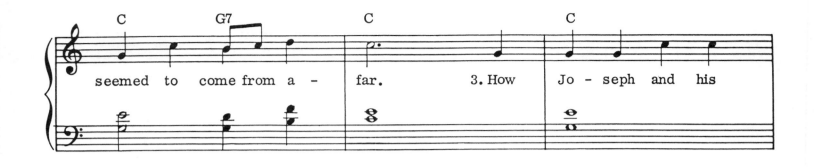

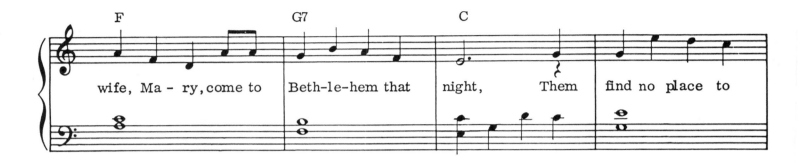

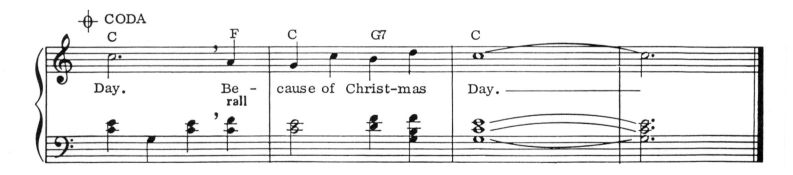

4. By and by they find a little nook
   In a stable all forlorn,
   And in a manger cold and dark,
   Mary's little boy was born.

5. Long time ago in Bethlehem,
   So the Holy Bible say,
   Mary's Boy Child, Jesus Christ,
   Was born on Christmas Day.

ROCKIN' AROUND
THE CHRISTMAS TREE

Words and Music by
JOHNNY MARKS

RUDOLPH THE RED-NOSED REINDEER

Words and Music by
JOHNNY MARKS

SANTA CLAUS IS COMIN' TO TOWN

Words by HAVEN GILLESPIE
Music by J FRED COOTS

THE TWELVE DAYS OF CHRISTMAS

TRADITIONAL

42

* Repeat this bar, in reverse order, as necessary

WE WISH YOU A MERRY CHRISTMAS

TRADITIONAL

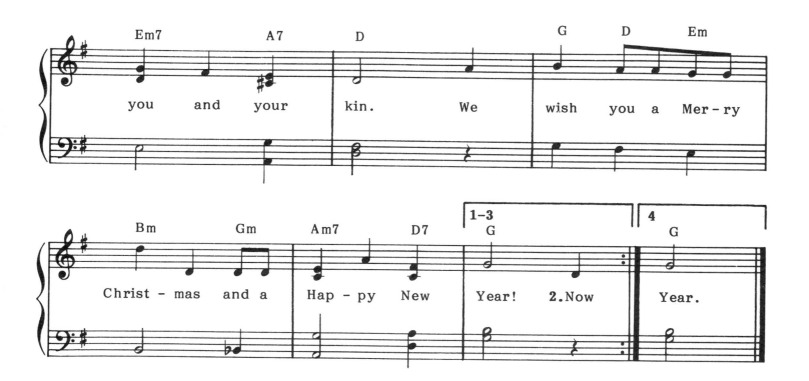

3. For we all like figgy pudding,
   For we all like figgy pudding,
   For we all like figgy pudding,
   So bring some out here.
   Good tidings we bring
   For you and your kin.
   We wish you a Merry Christmas
   And a Happy New Year.

4. And we won't go until we've got some,
   And we won't go until we've got some,
   And we won't go until we've got some,
   So bring some out here.
   Good tidings we bring
   For you and your kin.
   We wish you a Merry Christmas
   And a Happy New Year.

SLEIGH RIDE

Words by MITCHELL PARISH
Music by LEROY ANDERSON

WINTER WONDERLAND

Words by DICK SMITH
Music by FELIX BERNARD

Sleigh bells ring, are you list-'nin'? In the

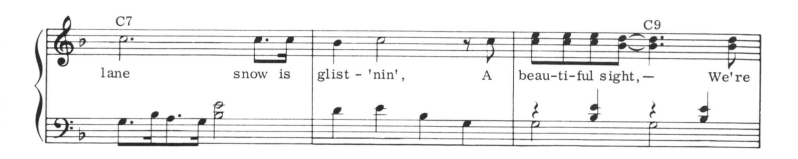

lane snow is glist-'nin', A beau-ti-ful sight,— We're

hap-py to-night,— walk-in' in a win-ter won-der-

-land! Gone a-way is the blue-bird, Here to

Printed in England
The Panda Group · Haverhill · Suffolk · 11/97

Also available

Take it easy

christmas carols

Easy arrangements for Piano

ORDER REF: 2193A

ISBN: 1-85909-194 6